My Bible

Jesus and the Storm

To

Brian and Bruce
Randy and Diana

And

all the boys and girls
who like Bible stories

BOOK 3

Friends

Jesus and the Children

By ETTA B. DEGERING

*Illustrated by Robert Berran
and Manning de V. Lee*

Published and Copyrighted © 1963 by the

REVIEW AND HERALD PUBLISHING ASSOCIATION
WASHINGTON, D.C.

OFFSET IN U.S.A.

Jesus and the Storm

Jesus stood in a boat—
    a fishing boat with oars and a sail—
    and talked to the many people
    who had come to hear Him.
All day long Jesus told them stories.
When it was evening Jesus said to His helpers,
    "Let us cross over to the other side
    of the lake and rest."

Jesus' helpers untied the boat.
They pushed it from the shore
  and raised the sail.
One man sat in the back of the boat
  to guide it with the steering tiller.
The boat moved slowly at first, and then faster
  across the quiet blue water.

A round yellow moon came up over the lake.
The stars twinkled high overhead.
Jesus was so very tired He lay down
    with His head on a pillow
    and was soon sound asleep.
The man at the back steered carefully.
The boat sailed on and on and on.

Suddenly a fierce wind began to blow.
It blew a black cloud over the moon.
It blew black clouds over the stars.
It whipped the water into huge angry waves.
The waves tossed the boat this way,
      and that way, and up and down.
There was lightning!
There was thunder!

The man at the tiller tried to steer the boat,
   but he couldn't.
Other men tried to row the boat with oars,
   but they couldn't.
Water filled the boat. It began to sink.
The men were afraid. They woke Jesus—
"Lord save us; we perish!" they cried.

Jesus heard their cry for help.
  He felt the angry wind.
  He saw the lightning flash.
  He heard the noisy thunder.
  But He was not afraid.
He stood up and said to the wind and waves,
              "Peace—be still."

The wind stopped blowing. The waves were still.
The clouds went away, and the stars twinkled again.
The boat sailed on the sparkling path
    that the moon made on the water,
    and crossed to the other side of the lake.
"Why were you afraid?" Jesus asked His helpers.
"Why were you afraid when I was with you?"

Jesus says to boys and girls today—
"Don't be afraid when the lightning flashes,
    and the thunder crashes,
    and the strong winds blow."
"I am with you always," says Jesus,
    "in the dark and in the storm,
I will never leave you. Don't be afraid."

Jesus and the Children

Mark and Sara were waiting
    with Mother and baby Esther
    to see Jesus.
Other children were waiting with their mothers.
Jesus' helpers frowned at them—
    "Can't you see that Jesus is busy?
    He has no time for children."

Mark and Sara, and Mother with baby Esther
turned slowly away.
Mark hung his head, and watched
the dust of the path squish up
between his brown toes.
Sara looked back at Jesus. A tear
ran down her cheek.

Then they heard Jesus say to His helpers,
   "Suffer the little children to come unto me,
   and forbid them not."
All the children ran to Jesus.
Jesus took baby Esther on His lap.
He smiled and touched Sara's cheek
   where the tear had run down.
He put His hand on Mark's head.
The children took turns standing close to Jesus.
   He told them stories.

On the way home Mark whistled a happy tune.
Sara skipped ahead, and then she waited
    and took Mother's hand.
"I wish we could see Jesus every day," she said.
"Maybe," said Mother, "maybe soon
    Jesus will come to the Temple."

One day Mark and Sara
    heard people singing the hosanna song.
They ran to see why the people were singing.
They saw Jesus riding on a colt
    coming down the road.
People were laying their coats on the road
    for Him to ride over.
Boys were waving palm branches and shouting.
Girls were tossing flowers and singing.

M. de V. Lee

"May we go with Jesus?" asked Mark.

"May we?" said Sara.

Mark's father cut a palm branch for him, and
　　Mother helped Sara fill a basket with flowers.

Mark waved his palm branch and shouted,
　　"Hosanna to the Son of David, Hosanna, Hosanna

Sara tossed flowers on the road and sang,
　　"Hosanna, Hosanna!"

It was like a big parade. It made Jesus happy
　　to hear the children shout and sing.

The parade came to the top of a hill.
Jesus stopped the colt,
    and looked down over the hill.
The boys stopped waving
    their palm branches and looked.
The girls stopped tossing flowers and looked.
All the people stopped
    and looked down over the hill.
What did they see down over the hill?

There was a brook down over the hill,
    a sing-along, laugh-along brook,
    but they were not looking at the brook.
There was a city with a high stone wall
    down over the hill,
    but they were not looking
    at the city with the high stone wall.

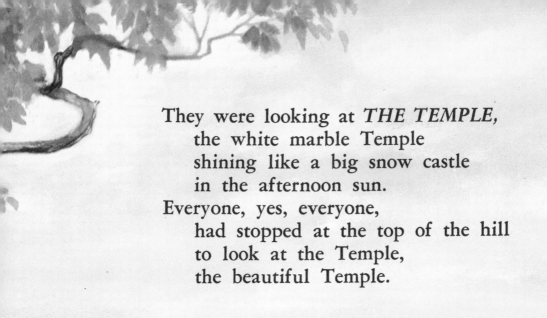

They were looking at *THE TEMPLE,*
   the white marble Temple
   shining like a big snow castle
   in the afternoon sun.
Everyone, yes, everyone,
   had stopped at the top of the hill
   to look at the Temple,
   the beautiful Temple.

The next day Mark and Sara and many other children
　　went with Jesus and His friends to the Temple.
But when they got there,
　　the sounds coming from the Temple
　　didn't sound like a Temple at all.
There was no sound of singing and praying.
It wasn't quiet-like and hush-like,
　　with people tiptoeing when they walked.
Instead—there was a terrible rackety noise!

Traders had brought to the Temple
   cattle and sheep and doves
   to sell for offerings.
They shouted, "Buy cattle for your offering."
   "Buy sheep for your offering."
   "Buy doves for your offering."
Moneychangers were there, clinking their money.
It didn't seem like a Temple at all—not at all.
It was like a noisy market place.

Jesus stood in the doorway—
The cattle traders looked at Him.
The sheep traders looked at Him.
The dove traders looked at Him.
They all stopped their shouting and selling.
The moneychangers stopped clinking their money.
Everyone looked at Jesus and waited
      to see what He would do.
Jesus raised His arm. He said,
      "TAKE THESE THINGS HENCE!"

Such a hurrying and a scurrying!
The traders hustled the cattle out.
They rushed the sheep out.
They grabbed the dove cages and ran.
The moneychangers didn't even stop
    to take their money.
All the grown-up people ran away from Jesus.

But the children didn't run away from Jesus.
Mark and Sara and all the children
    crowded close around Him.
Jesus told them stories.
He took the little ones on His knee.
A little boy went to sleep on His lap.

Then the sick people came to Jesus.
A boy with a hurt leg came hobbling on crutches.
Jesus put His hand on the hurt leg
    and made it well.
The boy threw away his crutches.
Now he could walk. He could run! He could jump

A father and mother brought
    their sick little girl to Jesus.
She was so sick they carried her in a hammock.
Jesus took her small thin hand in His. He said,
    "Be well, little girl, be well."
The little girl sat up and smiled. She was well.

A boy led a blind man to Jesus.
The blind man's eyes were tight shut.
He had never seen a tree or a house—not anything.
Jesus made his eyes see.
And the first thing the blind man ever saw
    was the lovely face of Jesus.

The children were so happy
    when they saw the sick people made well,
    they again waved palm branches
    and sang the hosanna song.
The grown-up people who had run away came back.
They looked in at the Temple doors
    and heard the children singing.
They said to Jesus, "Make the children be still."
But Jesus liked to hear the children sing.
He didn't want them to be still.

It was time to close the Temple doors.
Tomorrow the children would come back
    to hear more stories.
Jesus wanted them to come. He had said,
    "Suffer the little children to come unto me,
    and forbid them not."

Mark and Sara waved good-by to Jesus.
All the way home they sang the hosanna song,
   "*Hosanna to the Son of David,*
      Hosanna, Hosanna!"